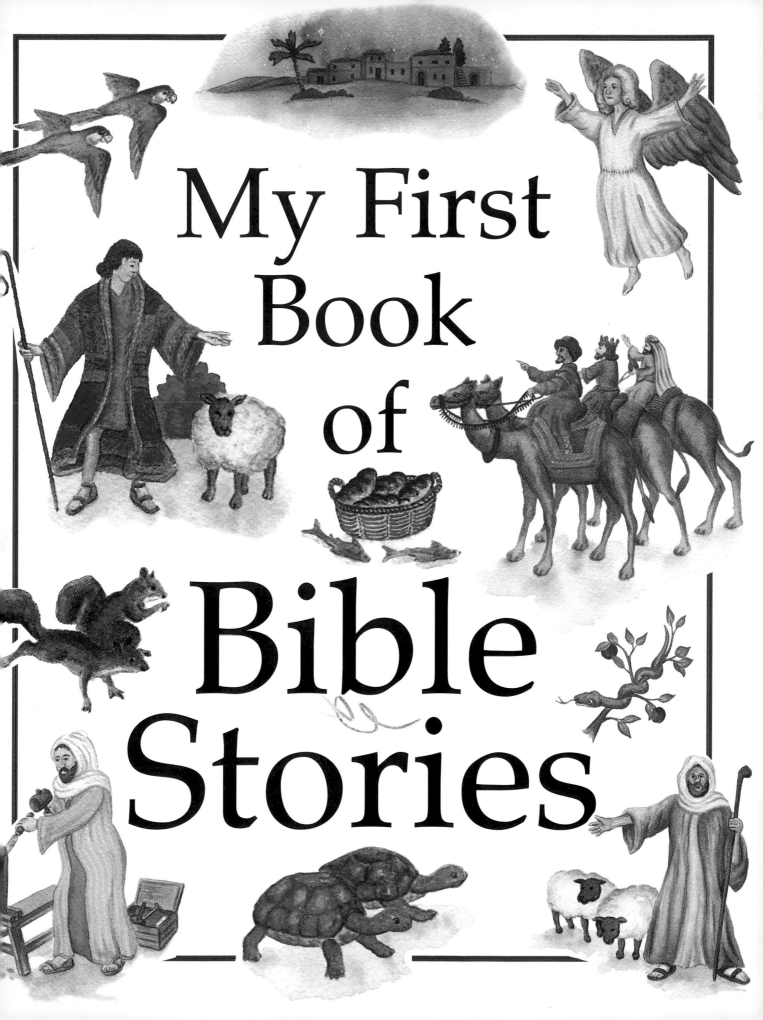

My First Book of Bible Stories

Published in 1999 by
Caxton Editions
16 Connaught Street
Marble Arch
London W2 2AF

© copyright 1999 Caxton Editions

Produced for Caxton Editions by
Open Door Limited
80 High Street
Colsterworth
Lincolnshire NG33 5JA

Editing: Kate Hughes
Illustration: Andrew Shepherd, Art Angle
Design: Open Door Limited
Colour Separation: GA Graphics, Stamford

Title: My First Book of Bible Stories
ISBN: 1-84067-062-2

Printed and bound by APP Printing Pte Ltd

My First
Book of
Bible Stories

stories rewritten by Hilary Hammond

CAXTON EDITIONS

Contents

OLD TESTAMENT

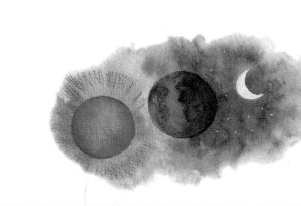

Contents

My First Book of Bible Stories

The Old

Testament

God Makes the World

God made this world of ours and it only took him six days. Imagine that!

Before God started work, everything was dark. There was no earth and no sky, no sun and no moon. There were no fields or trees, no houses and no people. There was nothing. There was just water and blackness and God's face.

The first thing God made was light. 'I shall call the light Day, and the darkness Night', God said, and he was pleased. 'I have made the first day', he said. Night passed and on the second day God made air. He called it Sky. Now there was water, light and air.

The next day God was very busy. He gathered together all the water and called it Sea. At the same time, he made dry land. He called this Earth. God was very pleased with his work. 'The earth can now grow plants', he said. 'Each plant will make seeds and from each seed more plants will grow.' God had great fun watching everything start to grow. This was day three.

On day four God made the sun, the moon and all the stars. A big, bright sun to light up the day, and the moon and millions of stars to come out at night. 'My world is beginning to look very good', said God.

The next day God had to get up very early, because he had lots to do. 'I am going to make creatures to live in the sea and the sky', he said. Into the sea he put starfish and seahorses, oysters and octopuses, whales and walruses, and fish of every size, shape and colour. He filled the sky with birds. Blue ones and pink ones, spotty ones and funny ones. Each one was different, and this was good.

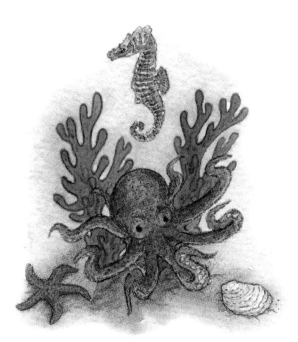

On day six God said, 'Now I must make some animals to live on the earth.' Cats with whiskers, spiders with eight legs and tigers with stripes, God made them all, big and small. Then God said, 'I am going to make some people', and so he made us!

That evening God looked out over the world and felt very happy. In just six days he had made such a lot that was good. His work was finished and on day seven he took a rest.

The Garden of Eden

This is the story of Adam and Eve. Just before everything in God's new world started to grow, a mist came over the earth. The mist watered the earth, and God took some dust from the ground. From this dust he made Adam and breathed life into his nose. Adam was ALIVE! He was the first man.

For Adam, God made a wonderful garden. He called it Eden and all sorts of amazing plants and every kind of tree grew in it. A river flowed through the garden and then divided into the four rivers, called Pishon, Gihon, Tigris and Euphrates.

But God had strong words for Adam. 'You may eat the fruit from any tree in the garden, but not from the tree of the knowledge of good and evil!'

Then God said, 'It is not good for you to be on your own. I will make you a helper.' So God set to work, and out of the ground he made all the animals and birds. When he had finished, he took them all to Adam, and Adam gave each one a name, but even among all these living things there was no helper.

So God went to work again. While Adam was fast asleep, he took out one of his ribs and from it he made Eve. She was the first woman. Adam and Eve got on very well together.

Of all the animals in the world the snake was the most nasty. One day it slid up to Eve and hissed, 'Why don't you try some of the fruit from the knowledge tree. It will make you as clever as God!'

Eve could not resist. She ate some of the fruit from the tree and then gave some to Adam.

Adam and Eve now knew many things that they had not known before. They saw that they had no clothes on and were ashamed. When they heard God walking in the garden, they ran and hid.

God was very angry. He knew that Adam and Eve had eaten from the knowledge tree. He cursed the snake and punished Adam and Eve. He was so angry that he threw them out of the garden.

Their wonderful life in the garden was over. From now on life would be much harder.

Then God sent angels to guard the garden of Eden and a sword of fire to protect the tree of life.

Noah's Ark

Once there was a good man and his name was Noah. When Noah was 500 years old he and his wife had three children. They were all boys and their names were Shem, Ham and Japheth.

God liked Noah and his family, but he was angry with all the other people in his world. Noah was kind and true and listened to God. The other people were bad and took no notice of God. They were always fighting.

'I must make the world a good place again', God said. 'I will send a great flood to wash away everything that is bad.'

'Noah, you must build a boat called an ark for yourself and your family. Make it good and strong. Use the very best wood. Give it a roof and fill it with rooms.'

God told Noah to take on to his ark two of every kind of animal, bird and insect. What a lot of rooms for Noah to build!

Noah worked on his boat every day. Days passed; weeks, months and years passed. Slowly the ark began to take shape.

'What are you doing Noah? Where is the water? Why are you building such a big boat?' his neighbours would call out to him. 'You must be mad', they laughed.

But Noah took no notice. He just kept on working.

At last the ark was finished. Noah loaded all the animals on board two by two:

monkeys, tigers, sheep, kangaroos, cats and mice, animals from all over the world. Imagine all the different colours and shapes, noises and smells.

The ark was completely full up. Then Noah loaded all the food, something to eat for everyone.

Then it started to rain. Soon the blue sky was full of black clouds. It rained and it rained and it didn't stop. As it rained the water rose and the ark began to float.

Forty days later the rain stopped. Noah went up on deck. All that he could see was water. 'I'll send my dove to see if there is any dry land', he said.

Off the dove went and when she came back she had a tiny olive leaf in her beak. Noah was happy. He knew the flood was nearly over.

A few days later, Noah's ark landed on dry land. He opened the giant doors and all the animals, birds and insects came out. Noah thanked God for keeping them all safe, and God promised never to flood the earth again.

And as a sign that he would always keep his promise, God put a rainbow in the sky.

Joseph and His Special Coat

There was once a man called Jacob who had many children. He loved them all, but his youngest son, Joseph, was his favourite. So he made him a special long coat with sleeves. This made Joseph's brothers jealous and they would not speak to him.

Now Joseph was a dreamer. One night he dreamed that all the wheat in the fields was bowing down to him. Another night he dreamed that all his brothers, the sun, moon and all the stars bowed down to him. You can guess what his brothers thought of that!

One day when they were all out in the fields working, Joseph's brothers made a plot to kill him. However, Reuben, one of the brothers, had a better idea. 'We don't need to kill him. Just take off his coat and throw him in a pit', he said. So that is what they did.

As it happened, some traders were passing by, and this gave the brothers an even better idea.

They pulled Joseph up out of the pit and sold him to the traders, who were on their way to Egypt.

Jacob thought Joseph was dead, and cried and cried for his lost son.

The traders sold Joseph to a rich Egyptian called Potiphar. At first everything went well. God was watching over Joseph and all that he did.

One of the King of Egypt's servants was also in prison. One night he had a dream and the next morning Joseph explained it to him. 'Your dream means that in three days the king will give you back your job', he said. Three days passed and Joseph was right, the servant was given his job back. 'Don't forget me', Joseph called to him as he left.

Potiphar was very pleased with Joseph, but his wife caused trouble by telling lies about Joseph.

Things went from bad to worse and this time Joseph was thrown into prison.

Joseph in Egypt

Two years passed and the king of Egypt began to have bad dreams. Who could tell him what they meant? He called together his wise men and magicians, but no one could help.

'I know!' the servant exclaimed. 'While I was in prison I met a man called Joseph. He will tell you exactly what the dreams mean.'

So the king called for Joseph and told him his dream. 'I was standing on the banks of the River Nile and seven fat cows came up out of the water. They were followed by seven thin cows.

The thin cows ate the fat cows, but you would not have known it, because the thin cows stayed thin.'

'This is the meaning of your dream', said Joseph. 'The seven fat cows are seven good years when there will be plenty to eat. The seven thin cows are seven bad years when there will be no food.'

lots of food. Seven years went by and, just as Joseph had said, in the eighth year the harvest failed. The whole world was short of food, there was a famine.

Word soon spread that there was food stored in Egypt. Joseph's father Jacob heard the news and sent all his sons, except Benjamin the youngest, to buy grain. When they bowed down before the governor of Egypt, they did not recognise Joseph, their own long-lost brother. He recognised them, of course, but he didn't let on.

In fact he accused them of being spies. Joseph was testing them. He told them they could take the grain, but in return they must bring Benjamin to him. Joseph held his brother Simeon as a prisoner while the other nine brothers returned home. Just before they left, Joseph secretly hid the money they had given him for the grain in the grain sacks.

'This is what you must do', Joseph continued. 'In the seven good years you must store up food for the seven bad years which will follow.'

The king was impressed. 'You are indeed a wise man, Joseph', he said, 'and I shall put you in charge of the whole of Egypt. '

Joseph went to work for the king of Egypt. He commanded the people to collect lots and

Time passed and all the food was eaten. Jacob had no choice but to send the brothers back to Egypt with Benjamin and twice the amount of money.

Once again the brothers stood before Joseph. He told them that God must have put the money back into their sacks. When he met Benjamin, his favourite brother Joseph felt very upset, but he still did not tell them that he was, Joseph, their long-lost brother.

That evening he held a party at his house for all his brothers. On the following morning the brothers were once again given sacks of grain and sent on their way. Once again each man's money was hidden in his sack. Joseph's silver cup was hidden in Benjamin's sack!

As soon as they had gone, Joseph sent his servant after them. He commanded the servant to search the sacks for his silver cup. The cup was found in Benjamin's sack.

Joseph many years ago, and how sad their father had been. 'If you take Benjamin away from us, our father will die of a broken heart', they pleaded.

The brothers were very upset. They knew that if they had to leave Benjamin behind as a prisoner, it would break their father's heart.

So they all went back to Joseph's house and pleaded with him. They told him everything about what they had done to their brother

Joseph could not stand it any longer. He cried and cried. Then he told them, 'I am Joseph! God has made me ruler over all of Egypt. Go and fetch our father so that we can all live together in this wonderful land.'

Moses in the Bulrushes

The king of Egypt was pleased with Joseph and all that he had done to save his people from the famine. He was kind to Joseph and his family, the people of Israel, who had come to live in his country.

Time passed and Egypt had a new king. By now many more Israelites were living in the country. Joseph had died and the Egyptians began to forget how he had saved them.

The new king did not like the Israelites. He thought that they would take over his country. So he was cruel to them and forced them to work as slaves. He made them build two great cities.

He became so angry that he decided to have every newborn Israelite baby boy killed.

Finally the day came when they could no longer hide their baby. He was growing big and strong and made so much noise that sooner or later someone would find out. So his mother had an idea. She made a basket out of reeds and covered it with tar so that it would float.

From then on every mother and father lived in fear. One Israelite family decided they would keep their baby boy. He was very precious to them, so they kept him hidden in their house for as long as they could.

Into this tiny boat she put her baby and then hid the basket in the tall reeds at the edge of the River Nile. 'Hide nearby and keep watch on your brother', she told her young daughter.

After a while, who should come along but the daughter of the king of Egypt. The princess had come to the river to have a wash. She had her servant girls with her. The baby's sister could hardly believe her eyes!

Suddenly the princess saw the basket! She sent her servant to fetch it and when she brought the basket back the princess opened it. There was the baby. He was crying and the princess felt very sorry for him. 'This is one of the Israelite babies!' she said.

Then the baby's sister stepped out of the reeds and asked if the princess would like her to find someone to look after the baby. 'Yes please', said the princess. So the sister ran and fetched her mother and the princess told her to look after the baby for her. She even paid the baby's mother to do it!

When the baby grew a bit older, the princess adopted him as her own son. She called him, Moses, a name which meant 'saved from the water.'

Crossing the Red Sea

The people of Israel were on the move. God had had enough of the wicked king of Egypt, who made his people work as slaves. Life in Egypt had become impossible!

So God chose Moses to go and speak to the king, but the king would not listen. The people of Israel listened to God and did as he commanded. The king of Egypt refused.

God sent plagues to punish Egypt. He sent millions of frogs, flies and locusts. He also sent hail and darkness, but the king was stubborn and would not give in. He would not let the people go!

God became very angry. He killed some Egyptians and finally the king agreed to let the Israelites go. Quickly Moses got the people ready to leave. They were going to travel across the desert to the Red Sea. God would show them the way. By day he would be like a pillar of cloud in the sky; by night he would be like a pillar of fire.

After the Israelites had left, the king of Egypt changed his mind. He called together his army of 600 chariots and sent them to catch the Israelites. 'They will not get away!' he shouted angrily.

By now the Israelites had reached the shores of the Red Sea. When they saw clouds of dust behind them they knew the Egyptians were coming after them. Everyone was very frightened.

'What have you done, Moses! Why have you brought us here? We are all going to die!' they cried, but Moses stayed calm. 'Don't be afraid', he said. 'Trust God, he will fight for you.'

Then God said to Moses, 'Lift up your stick and put your hand out over the sea. It will divide to let the people through.'

That night the pillar of cloud moved so that it was between the Israelites and the Egyptians. There was so much cloud and darkness, the soldiers couldn't see a thing.

Moses put his hand out over the sea. God drove the water back with a strong east wind.

There was now dry land where the sea had been. Imagine! A dry path through the sea, with giant walls of water on either side.

All the Israelites crossed safely to the other side, but when the Egyptians tried to follow, the sea suddenly closed in on them.

All the soldiers were swept away by the foaming water.

Samson and the Lion

Once there was a man called Manoah whose wife could not have any children. One day an angel appeared to Manoah's wife and said, 'You are going to have a baby. You must look after yourself and only eat and drink good things.'

The angel told Manoah's wife that she was going to have a baby boy. She must never, ever cut his hair, because he was going to be very special. He was going to be God's child.

After nine months Manoah's wife gave birth to a big, bouncy baby boy. She called him Samson.

Samson grew up to be a handsome young man with long, flowing hair. One day he saw a beautiful young woman and when he got home he told his parents that he wanted to marry her.

But there was a problem. The girl was a Philistine and Samson was an Israelite. The Philistines were ruling Israel at this time, which caused a bad feeling between them and the Israelite people. 'Surely you can find an Israelite girl to marry, Samson', his mother and father pleaded, but Samson's mind was made up.

Finally, Samson's parents agreed to go with him to visit the girl and her family, who lived in a city called Timnah. On the way they stopped at a vineyard. While his mother and father were having a rest, Samson wandered off through the trees.

Suddenly, from out of nowhere, a young lion came roaring towards him.

Quick as a flash Samson grabbed hold of the lion and tore it apart with his bare hands.

He could hardly believe what he had done! How could he have killed the lion? Was he really this strong? Samson was frightened, so he kept quiet and did not tell anyone what had happened.

A few days later Samson returned to marry his beautiful bride. On the way he stopped to look at the body of the lion. To his surprise he found that a

swarm of bees had nested in it. What was more, the bees had made some honey.

Using his bare hands Samson scooped out some honey. It tasted really good. What a nice snack to eat while he was walking along!

Samson gave some honey to his parents as well, but he decided not to tell them where he had got it.

David and Goliath

The Israelites fought many battles against the Philistines, who were bad people because they had turned away from God. One of the battles was won by a surprising hero whose name was David.

Imagine a wide valley with mountains on both sides. On one side stood the Philistines, on the other side stood the Israelites. The two armies waited and watched each other. Who would attack first?

Then a giant man marched out of the Philistine camp and into the valley. His name was Goliath. He wore a huge bronze helmet and a heavy, bronze coat of armour. The handle of his spear was as thick as a pole. Strong men shook with fear when they saw its heavy iron head.

Goliath's voice boomed out. 'Israel, send out a man to fight with me! If he wins, then Israel wins. If I win, the Philistines win. Come on', he continued, 'what are you frightened of? Send out a man!'

For 40 days Goliath came out to challenge the Israelites, but no soldier dared to go out and fight with him.

Now there was a man called Jesse and he had three sons. His youngest son was called David. David was not a great soldier, he was a shepherd, but sometimes Jesse would send him to take food to the Israelite army.

One day when David arrived at the camp, Goliath was in the valley shouting out his challenge. David stopped to listen. He was interested. He had an idea.

'Let me go and fight with the Philistine', he said.

'You!' the Israelites laughed. 'You are just a boy. How could you possibly win?' But David went on asking and Saul, the commander of the Israelite army, ordered his men to get David ready for battle. They dressed him in bronze armour, but the armour was too heavy. David could not even walk.

'This is no good', said David, and off came the armour. David bent down and picked up five smooth stones from the river and put them in his bag. With his catapult in his hand he looked more like a shepherd than a soldier, but he walked out to meet Goliath.

Goliath could not believe his eyes. He laughed at David and poked fun at him, but David stood firm. 'I have God on my side', he said, 'and I will kill you, Goliath.'

This made the giant angry and he marched forward to attack. Quickly, David let loose a stone from his catapult. It hit Goliath straight between the eyes and he dropped to the ground.

David finished the giant off with his own sword. The Israelites jumped for joy and the Philistines ran for their lives. What a victory!

Jonah and the Big Fish

There was once a man called Jonah who did not want to do what God told him.

God told Jonah to go to a city called Nineveh and tell the people there to stop being so bad. However, Jonah did just the opposite. He went to Joppa, a city by the sea. Here he found a ship going to Tarshish. 'I know, I'll go there instead', Jonah thought. 'God will never find me there!'

But God knew exactly where Jonah was. As the ship sailed away God sent a big storm out over the sea.

The sailors were used to bad weather, but this storm was really bad. The ship tossed up and down on huge waves.

It didn't look as if they would make it to land!

The sailors were very afraid. They started throwing the cargo overboard to make the ship lighter, so that it would not sink, but it was no good, the storm was too strong.

All the sailors prayed to their gods, but still the storm raged. Finally the captain went to find Jonah. He was fast asleep! 'Wake up, Jonah!' the captain cried. 'The storm will sink the ship, you must pray to your god. Perhaps he will save us!'

Jonah knew God had sent the storm because he had run away. He told the sailors what he had done and they were very frightened. Jonah told them to throw him into the sea. 'That will stop the storm', he said.

The sailors did not want to throw Jonah over the side of the ship. They did not want to kill him, but the storm was going to sink the ship, and the sailors were very afraid of Jonah's god, so over the side Jonah went. In an instant the sea was calm.

Jonah bobbed up and down in the water. Suddenly a giant fish appeared, as big as the biggest whale. God had sent the fish to swallow Jonah.

Gulp! Down the fish's throat Jonah went and into its stomach.

He stayed in the stomach of the fish for three days and three nights. It was very dark, very wet and very scary.

Jonah prayed to God. He prayed and prayed. He promised to do what God told him.

Then God spoke to the giant fish. The fish waved its giant tail and spat Jonah out of its stomach and on to dry land.

From then on Jonah did exactly what God told him.

The New

Testament

Baby Jesus is Born

At Christmas we celebrate the birth of a very special baby. His name is Jesus. He was born a long, long time ago in a town called Bethlehem in Judaea. Judaea was a very hot and dusty country with many mountains.

Like much of the world at that time, Judaea was ruled by the Romans, King Herod and all his people had to obey the Roman Emperor, who was called Caesar.

One day Caesar sent an order to all his people, telling them to go to the towns and write their names in a big book. They also had to write down everything they owned. Caesar wanted to know just how big his empire was. Everyone had to obey his order.

Mary and Joseph were two of the many people who had to go and sign the book. They lived in a town called Nazareth, but the Emperor ordered them to travel miles and miles to Bethlehem to sign their names.

Mary was going to have a baby. God had sent the angel Gabriel to tell her the good news. Another angel visited Joseph, telling him to take very special care of Mary.

When Mary and Joseph arrived at Bethlehem, after a hard journey, there was nowhere for them to stay. The town was full of people. They had walked such a long way, but now the only place they could find to sleep was a stable.

That night Mary had her baby. Imagine what the animals in the stable must have thought: a tiny little baby lying asleep on their straw!

Up on the hills above Bethlehem, some shepherds were looking after their sheep. It was cold that night. The shepherds looked down at the town, up at the sky and out at the sheep. Everywhere was very quiet. Suddenly they saw an angel and the sky was full of light. They were very frightened, but the angel said, 'Do not be afraid, I have some good news for you. Jesus is born.' And the angel told them where to find the baby.

Then the sky filled with music. Hundreds of angels were singing and dancing. The shepherds couldn't believe their eyes!

Quickly the shepherds hurried down the hill and through the narrow streets of the town. When they reached the stable, there was baby Jesus all wrapped up warm and snug. It was just like the angel had told them!

The Three Wise Men

Look up at the sky on a clear night and you will see millions of stars. People have always watched the stars. Wise men watch the stars so that they can learn from them – they want to understand our world.

Long ago in the East there lived three wise men. Their names may have been Balthazar, Caspar and Melchior. Every night they watched the sky and filled page after page of their notebooks with all that they saw.

One night they were amazed to see a bright new star in the sky, the brightest star they had ever seen. They were very excited.

The star led the three wise men to Jerusalem. Here there was someone else who had heard the news. He too was a king, and his name was Herod. Now Herod was rather upset.

'This can only mean one thing', said Balthazar. 'Yes', said Melchior, 'the new King has been born.' 'Then we must follow the star', said Caspar. 'It will lead us to where he is.'

So that very night the three wise men set off on their long journey. Their camels were a bit grumpy, because they had just settled down for a good sleep.

'If anyone is king around here, it is me. I am the king of Judaea!', he exclaimed. 'But Sir', said his priests, 'people say that a new king will be born in Bethlehem and will rule over all of Israel.'

Herod was a cunning man and he secretly sent for the three wise men.

'Go to Bethlehem and search until you find the child', he told them. 'Then come back and tell me exactly where he is, so that I can go and worship him.'

The three wise men set off again, and once more the star showed them the way. When it stopped they knew their search was over. They climbed down from their weary camels and went in to the house.

There was the baby Jesus with Mary, his mother. What a sight! A tiny child and these three splendid men. The wise men bowed down. They knew they had found their King. From their dusty bags they took presents, of gold, frankincense and myrrh, and gave them to Jesus.

Of course, they should have returned to Herod, but in a dream God warned them that Herod meant to hurt the baby. So they went home, but not the same way as they had come.

Jesus and His Disciples

When Jesus was a young man he was baptised with water, standing in the River Jordan. As he came out of the river God's spirit came down from heaven and blessed him.

It was time for Jesus to go out into the world and tell everybody about the Kingdom of God. His work was to spread goodness and truth throughout the whole world.

One day, Jesus was walking beside Lake Galilee with a lot of other people. He saw two fishing boats and had an idea. He went up to the fishermen, who were washing their nets, and asked if he could use one of the boats, the one which belonged to a man called Simon.

Simon agreed and sailed his boat out a little way from the shore. Now Jesus could carry on teaching the people who had come from everywhere to see him.

Afterwards Jesus told Simon to sail out to the deep water so that they could catch some fish. 'I've fished all night and caught nothing!' Simon replied. 'But if you say so, then I will do it.'

Over the side went the nets, and when Simon pulled them back in they were full of fish. There were so many fish that his nets started to break.

Simon and his friends, James and John, were amazed. 'Don't be afraid', Jesus said to Simon. 'Come with me, and I will teach you to catch men instead of fish.'

So Simon dropped his nets and followed Jesus. James and John, who were brothers, also dropped their nets and followed Jesus, leaving behind their father Zebedee.

The four men walked to Capernaum and went into the synagogue. Jesus began to teach and people were amazed by what he said. Who was this man? He was not a regular priest or scribe, but everything he said made so much sense.

This was not all. With a few words Jesus healed a man and made him better. The news spread fast through the whole of Galilee. People could hardly believe their eyes.

And so it went on. Jesus cured Simon's mother-in-law and many, many more people with all kinds of illnesses. A scribe came up to Jesus and said, 'Teacher, I will follow you wherever you go.' Jesus said to him, 'Foxes have holes and birds have nests, but I don't have a home.' Jesus was always on the move. He never stayed in one place for long.

Jesus did many special things. He cured a man who could not walk and made blind people see again. Crowds came from everywhere to see him. 'Follow me', he called out to Matthew the tax collector as he walked past him, and Matthew too followed Jesus.

Jesus gathered together twelve special friends. These were his disciples and their names were: Simon (who was also called Peter) and Andrew, James and John, Philip, Bartholomew, Matthew, Thomas, James the son of Alphaeus, Thaddaeus, Simon from Cana, and Judas Iscariot.

Feeding the Five Thousand

Jesus and his disciples had been very busy. They were tired and needed a rest. So Jesus decided they should take a boat across Lake Galilee to a peaceful, quiet place where they could be alone.

But as the little boat crossed the water, hundreds of people ran along the shore to meet it. Everybody wanted to meet Jesus. They had heard stories about him healing the sick and wanted to see the special things he could do.

crowd began to get a little restless. Tummies were starting to rumble. 'Jesus', said the disciples, 'the people need to eat! We need to eat! Send the crowd to the villages to buy some food.' But Jesus said, 'Why can't you buy them some food? You've got money.'

When they arrived at the other side of the lake, Jesus gathered everyone around him. He began talking to the people and teaching them many things. Time flew by. Everybody listened hard to what he had to say.

'Yes, but not nearly enough to feed all these people! There are thousands of them!' the disciples exclaimed.

'Well, what have you got?' said Jesus patiently.

The sun slowly dropped in the sky and still everyone listened. It was not until the evening that one or two people in the

The disciples went away and had a look. 'Just five loaves and two fish', they said when they came back.

Now Jesus really was a special person. He sat the crowd down in groups, all five thousand of them. Then he took the five loaves and the two fish and, looking up to heaven, he blessed them.

gave it to his disciples to share out, and as he did so, more and more bread appeared. The same happened with the fish.

What happened next was amazing! Suddenly there was enough food for everyone. Jesus broke the bread and

So all the people ate until they were full. To everyone's surprise, when the disciples went around afterwards collecting up the left-overs, they found they had twelve baskets full of pieces of bread and fish. No one could believe their eyes.

It was a miracle!

Jesus Walks on Water

Do you know anyone who can walk on water? Jesus could! This is the story of how he did it.

Late one day, Jesus told his disciples to take a boat out across Lake Galilee. The men crowded into the boat. Jesus stood on the shore to see them off. 'Go on ahead', he said. 'I'll meet you on the other side of the lake.'

When everyone had gone, Jesus climbed a hill to find a quiet place to pray to God on his own. He stayed there a long time. It had been a busy day and he had a lot to say to God.

Meanwhile, out on the lake a storm was beginning. Night had fallen and it was very dark. The waves that had gently lapped against the side of the boat now crashed against it. The men in the boat were starting to get frightened. It was difficult to control the boat.

But wait! What's this coming towards them, across the roaring waves? The disciples in the boat rubbed their eyes. They could not believe it! They called to one another and everyone came to the side to look. 'Jesus is coming!' they shouted. 'And he's walking on the water!'

Then they started to get really frightened. 'What if he's a ghost!' they said, their knees shaking with fear.

'Don't be afraid',
a voice called from
across the water.
'It's me, Jesus.'

'If it really is you', Peter
replied, 'then let me come to
you on the water.'

'Come' Jesus said.

So Peter climbed out over
the side of the boat and
stepped carefully on to the
water. The dark black water
took his weight! He could
hardly believe it. Carefully he
took a step. Then another.

Then he started walking
towards Jesus.

'I can walk on water too!' Peter thought, but then a gust of wind and a crashing wave made him look away from Jesus. Suddenly he was afraid. It was then that he began to sink.

'Help, Lord, save me!' Peter cried out. Jesus stretched out his arm and Peter caught hold of his hand. 'Why did you get scared?' Jesus said.

Soon both men were safely in the boat. Everyone looked up. The wind had died away and the lake was calm. All the disciples turned to Jesus and worshiped him.

The Good Samaritan

One day when Jesus was busy teaching, a lawyer asked him a question. 'What must I do to be given eternal life and live forever?' he asked. Jesus replied, 'What have you been told? What do the books say?'

'That I should love the Lord my God with all my soul, all my strength and all my mind, and love my neighbour as much as I love myself', said the lawyer.

'That is the right answer', said Jesus.

But the man wanted to know more. 'Who is my neighbour?' he asked. So Jesus told him the story of the Good Samaritan. This is what he said.

A man was travelling from Jerusalem to Jericho when a gang of robbers jumped out and attacked him. They pushed him to the ground, kicked him and then ran off, leaving him lying in the road.

The man was so badly hurt that he could not get up. He lay in the road moaning and groaning and wishing that someone would come along to help him.

It was a very hot day. The sun was beating down.

Just by chance a priest came along the road. He saw the injured man but did not stop. The priest was in a hurry and so he walked past on the other side of the road.

A little later another man, who was a Levite, came along, but he too had better things to do, and walked past on the other side of the road.

The third person to come along was a man from Samaria, a Samaritan. When he saw the man lying in the road he ran to help him.

He bandaged the man's wounds and took him to town on his own donkey.

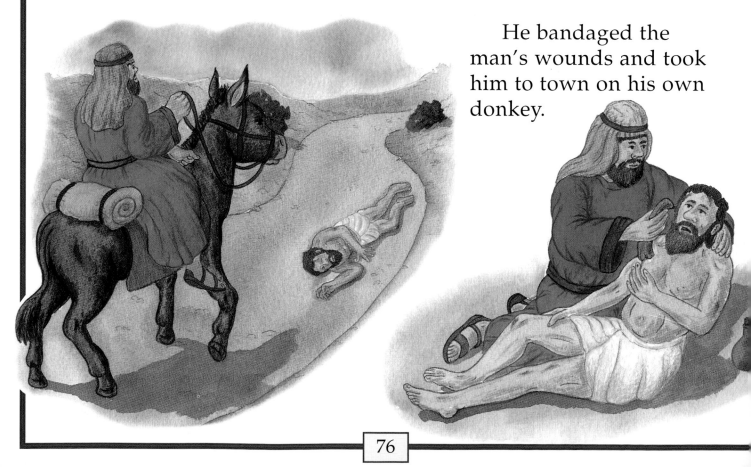

The Samaritan was such a kind man that he found an inn where the injured man could stay, and spent the night taking care of him.

In the morning he gave the innkeeper two silver coins and asked him to look after the poor man.

'Now', said Jesus, 'which of these three men was a good neighbour?'

'Why, the Samaritan, of course!' replied the lawyer.

Jesus told the lawyer to go and behave like the Samaritan.

Jesus and the Little Children

People loved to listen to what Jesus had to say. They came from the towns and the villages, from near and far to hear him talk.

Sometimes people brought their children to Jesus. 'Please touch our little children', they would call out. They knew that if Jesus touched their children and prayed for them, then everything would be all right.

This made the disciples cross. Jesus had more than enough to do. He should not be spending time with little children when there were so many people who needed his help.

So the disciples began telling the people to stop bringing their children to see Jesus.

When Jesus found out what was happening, he was not at all happy with his friends. 'Let the children come and see me', he told them firmly. 'You must not stop them.

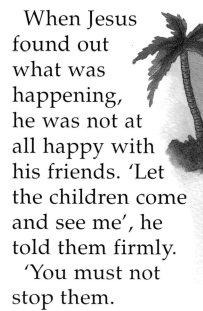

The Kingdom of God belongs to people who are just like these little children.'

Then Jesus put his big strong arms around all the children and blessed them.

'Be careful. Don't think that little children are worth nothing', Jesus once told a crowd of people.

'They all have angels in Heaven and God looks after each and every one of them.'

Jesus loved children. He made many sick children better. One day a man came to him who had a son who was ill. 'Please help me, my son has epilepsy and is suffering very much', he pleaded with Jesus.

'He often falls on to the fire or into the water. I brought him to the disciples but they could not cure him', he continued.

The man was crying. He was very upset.

Jesus told the man to bring his son to him. He gave a strong command and in an instant the boy was better. It was a miracle!

The Last Supper

Jesus lived a good life. His teaching and healing made many people very happy. He taught people a great deal about God, his father.

Jesus always did what God wanted him to do. Now the time came when he had to die. God wanted his son back home in Heaven.

It was two days before the great festival called the Passover. Caiaphas, who was the high priest, had called together all the chief priests and elders. They did not like Jesus, because people seemed to take more notice of him than they did of them. They plotted to have Jesus arrested and killed. It would have to be done quietly, with no fuss.

Luckily for Caiaphas, one of the disciples was looking for a way to earn some extra money. Judas agreed to hand Jesus over to the chief priests. His payment would be thirty pieces of silver.

When the day came to celebrate the Passover, Jesus told his disciples where they would all eat that evening.

'Go into the city and a man carrying a jar of water will meet you. He will lead you to a large upstairs room. That is where we are going to have our supper', Jesus said.

Later in the day, Jesus and his disciples sat down in the upstairs room to eat their last supper together. While they were sitting, Jesus got up and began to wash the feet of his friends. The disciples were puzzled and felt embarrassed, but Jesus did not stop. He washed everybody's feet except one – Judas. He knew that Judas was going to betray him, by handing him over to the chief priests. As they were all watching, Jesus took some bread and broke it and gave each man a piece. 'This is my body', he said. In the same way, he drank wine from a cup and then passed the cup to his disciples, saying: 'This is my blood. Remember me when you eat bread and drink wine like this.'

By now the disciples knew that something was about to happen. Something was not quite right. 'One of you is going to betray me and I am going to die', Jesus said. His friends were very upset and frightened. 'Is it I, Lord?' each said in turn.

Only Judas, with his hard heart, knew the terrible truth.

Peter and the
Crow of the Cock

After the last supper, Jesus and the disciples walked to a small hill called the Mount of Olives. Night was falling. The air was full of wonderful smells and sounds.

Jesus knew that Judas was going to betray him. Time was running out. He warned the disciples that when he was gone, they would find it difficult to go on obeying his rules.

Peter spoke up, saying that he would never turn away from Jesus. What Jesus said shocked him. 'Tonight, before the cock crows, you will deny me three times.'

Jesus then took the disciples to a garden called Gethsemane and asked them to wait while he went to pray. He was frightened, so he

asked Peter, James and John to stay close by.

When Jesus came back to his three friends he found that they were all fast asleep. 'Peter, couldn't you stay awake for just one hour!' he said.

He went to pray again, and when he returned he found the same thing. Three men, chins on chests, fast asleep. Were they snoring?

Jesus went off to pray for a third time. Once again they were asleep when he returned. 'Come on', he said, 'Get up. It's time to go.'

of the men Judas would kiss, because that was his secret sign.

'Greetings, Master!' Judas said, and he kissed Jesus. 'Seize him!' yelled the crowd. There was a scuffle. One of the men with Jesus drew his sword and cut off the ear of the high priest's slave.

Suddenly Judas appeared. Behind him was a great crowd waving swords and truncheons. They were watching to see which

'Put your sword away', commanded Jesus. 'With one word to God I could put a stop to all this, but it is meant to happen. God wants it.' When they heard this his disciples turned and ran away.

But Peter followed Jesus as he was led to Caiaphas.While the high priest questioned Jesus, Peter sat outside in the courtyard.

A maid who happened to be walking by stopped and looked at Peter. 'You were with Jesus, weren't you?' she said.

'No, no, not me', said Peter. 'You are wrong.'

When more people came by and said the same thing, Peter became angry. 'I do not know the man', he shouted.

And then it happened. The cock crowed. Peter remembered what Jesus had said. He knew that he had betrayed his very best friend. He cried and cried.

The First Easter

This is the story of the last few days that Jesus spent on our earth. Jesus was arrested and taken to Pontius Pilate, who was the governor. The priests said that Jesus was a bad man. The disciples and many other people said that he was a good man. Pilate had to decide who was right.

It was very difficult. He just did not know what to do. Then he had an idea. At the feast of the Passover it was traditional to let one prisoner out of jail.

Pilate had two prisoners in front of him. One was Jesus and the other was a very nasty man called Barabbas. He was sure that if he asked the crowd which one to free, they would choose Jesus. No one liked Barabbas. Pilate thought that this was the best thing to do.

But he was wrong. The chief priests had been busy turning people against Jesus. The crowd shouted for Barabbas to be set free. Pilate was very shocked and turned away. 'You have made this choice', he said, 'not me.'

And so the Roman soldiers took Jesus away. 'Hail, King of the Jews', they mocked, and they put a crown made of twigs with sharp thorns on his head, but still Pilate did not want to kill him.

Once more he took Jesus out to the crowd. He was met with angry shouts. 'Kill him, kill him', the people yelled. Finally, Pilate gave in and sentenced Jesus to be killed by being nailed to a wooden cross.

But wait! Our story does not end here. This is what happens. . .

Jesus was made to carry his own cross. He was taken to a hill called the Place of the Skull. There the Roman soldiers nailed him to the cross. Two other men who were robbers were also nailed to crosses. Sobbing, Jesus' mother Mary watched helplessly as Jesus slowly died.

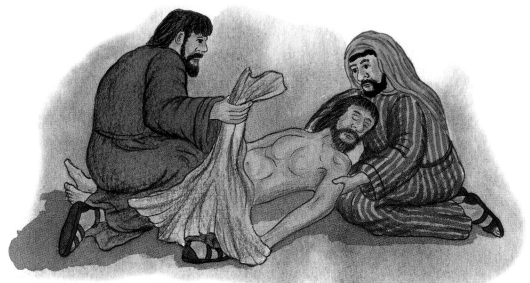

Pilate gave the body of Jesus to a man called Joseph of Arimathea. Joseph and his friend Nicodemus took the body, wrapped it in strips of cloth scented with spices and put it in a new grave which Joseph had made. They rolled a great big heavy rock against the door to block it shut.

A short time later Mary Magdalene went to visit the tomb. Something was not quite right. The stone had been rolled away and where the body had been there were now only strips of cloth. Mary ran to fetch Peter and another of the disciples.

Sure enough, when the men reached the tomb they found things just as Mary had said.

Simon and his friend had to go home, but Mary stayed by the tomb. As she cried softly to herself, she bent down to look inside again. To her amazement she saw two angels sitting where Jesus had been, their clothes and wings shining the brightest white!

Mary looked around and, suddenly there beside her stood a man. 'Why are you crying?' he asked gently. Mary wondered if he was a gardener. She explained that she was crying because Jesus was gone.

'Mary', the man said. Mary looked up into the man's face. It was Jesus! He was alive!

An A-Z of
Bible Characters

ADAM AND EVE – Adam was the first man God made and Eve was the first woman. They  lived together in the beautiful Garden of Eden.

ANGEL GABRIEL – Gabriel was a special messenger angel. God sent him to tell Mary that she was going to have a baby. He would be a very special baby, and his name would be Jesus.

BARABBAS – Barabbas was a very bad man, and he had been put in prison. When Pilate asked the crowd which prisoner they wanted him to set free they chose Barabbas and not Jesus. This happened during the feast of Passover.

BENJAMIN – The youngest of Jacob's twelve sons. It was because of Benjamin that Jacob found his most  famous son, Joseph. Benjamin found a silver cup in his sack of grain when he was leaving Egypt.

CAESAR – Caesar was the name of a famous Roman family. It was used as the title of the Roman emperors. Augustus Caesar was the first Roman emperor and ruled Judaea when Jesus was born. Tiberius Caesar was ruler during the last half of Jesus' life.

CAIAPHAS – Caiaphas was the High Priest. He plotted with the chief priests to kill Jesus. He was frightened because the people listened to Jesus and not to him.

DAVID – When he was a young man, David killed a Philistine giant called Goliath. He went on to become the greatest king of Israel. Jesus is called the Son of David, because he was born into David's family.

THE DISCIPLES – Jesus' closest friends and followers were called disciples. There were twelve of them and their names were: Simon (who was also called Peter) and Andrew, James and John, Philip, Bartholomew, Matthew, Thomas, James the son of Alphaeus, Thaddaeus, Simon from Cana, and Judas Iscariot. Peter and Andrew were brothers. James and John were the sons of Zebedee and were both fishermen. Philip was from Bethsaida, where Peter and Andrew also lived. Matthew was a tax collector. Thomas is sometimes called 'doubting Thomas' because he didn't believe that Jesus had come back to life after he died until he saw Jesus himself. Judas led the Roman soldiers to Jesus and was paid thirty pieces of silver for doing so. Later, he felt so miserable about what he had done that he killed himself.

GOD – God is the father of Jesus and of all human beings. He made the world and everything in it. The Bible is called 'the Word of God' because Christians believe it is God's real words, written down by men and women.

GOLIATH – Goliath was the champion of the Philistine army. He was a giant of a man, but he was beaten by a young Israelite shepherd called David.

THE GOOD SAMARITAN – This man saved the life of a traveller who had been attacked and left for dead by a band of robbers. 'Samaritan' was the name given to a person who came from Samaria. Today 'The Samaritans' is an organisation that helps people who are in trouble.

HEROD THE GREAT – This man was king of Judaea when Jesus was born. He tried to kill Jesus. People called Jesus 'king' and Herod did not like it.

JACOB – Jacob had twelve sons and each one was the head of one of the twelve tribes of Israel. The Israelites were God's chosen people. Jacob is sometimes called 'Israel' because he was father of the people of Israel.

JESSE – Jesse was David's father. David was his youngest son. Some of his other sons were soldiers. Jesse lived in Bethlehem in Judaea.

JESUS – Jesus is God's son. The New Testament is the story of Jesus' life. Jesus was a Jew and he lived near Lake Galilee. He was 32 years old when he died. He died to show the people of the world how much God loved them.

JONAH – This man ran away from God and was swallowed by a giant fish. He lived to tell the tale and spent the rest of his life telling people about God.

JOSEPH – Joseph was Jacob's favourite son. His father made him a special coat. Joseph became ruler of the whole of Egypt. He was a very clever man who could understand dreams. He saved Egypt when there was a famine.

JOSEPH OF ARIMATHEA – This Joseph made the tomb in which Jesus was laid after he had died. He was a very important person and was a member of the Jewish council.

MANOAH – Manoah was Samson's father.

MARY AND JOSEPH – Mary and Joseph were the mother and father of Jesus. Mary was specially chosen by God. Joseph was from a town called Nazareth, in Galilee, and he was a carpenter. He was a good man.

MARY MAGDALENE – Mary was from a place called Magdala and was a follower of Jesus. She was the first person to see Jesus after he came back to life.

MOSES – Moses was the baby the princess of Egypt found in the bulrushes – his name means 'saved from the water'. When he grew up, Moses was chosen by God to lead the people of Israel out of Egypt.

NOAH – Noah was the man who built a giant boat to escape God's great flood. His ark was about 450 feet long and into it went every kind of animal that lived on the earth. Noah was helped by his three sons, Shem, Ham and Japheth.

PONTIUS PILATE – Pilate was the Roman governor of Judaea. Jesus was taken to him after he had been arrested. Pilate talked to Jesus for a long time and could find nothing wrong with what he said.

POTIPHAR – This man was a captain in the Egyptian army. He bought Joseph from the traders to be his slave.

REUBEN – Reuben was one of Joseph's brothers. He persuaded his brothers not to kill Joseph, but to sell him to the traders instead.

SAMSON – Samson was an Israelite. He was very, very strong and once killed a lion. He lost all his strength when a woman called Delilah cut off all his hair.

SIMEON – Simeon was another of Jacob's sons. He was held prisoner in Egypt by his brother Joseph while his brothers went to fetch Benjamin.

THREE WISE MEN – These three men were extremely clever. They spotted a very bright star and followed it. It led them to the baby Jesus. Their names may have been Balthazar, Caspar and Melchior. They came from the East.

ZEBEDEE – This man was the father of James and John, two of Jesus' disciples. He was a fisherman on Lake Galilee.